High-Frequency READERS™

D1283306

LUNCH

Written by Gay Su Pinnell
Illustrated by David Bamundo

Scholastic Inc.
New York   Toronto   London   Auckland   Sydney
Mexico City   New Delhi   Hong Kong

ISBN 0-439-13186-3

12

5/0
Printed in China   62

I like apples.

I like sandwiches.

I like bananas.

I like pizza.

I like cookies.

I like milk.

I like lunch.